CRISIS IN SPACE

MAKE YOUR OWN ADVENTURE WITH
DOCTOR WHO
CRISIS IN SPACE

by Michael Holt

SEVERN **SH** HOUSE

This first world edition published in Great Britain by
SEVERN HOUSE PUBLISHERS Ltd of
4 Brook Street, London W1Y 1AA

By arrangement with the British Broadcasting Corporation

Acknowledgements to Colin Baker as the Doctor, Nicola Bryant
as Peri and Mark Strickson as Turlough

British Library Cataloguing in Publication Data

Holt, Michael
    Crisis in space. — (Make your own adventure
    with Doctor Who)
    I. Title   II. Bennett, Gail   III. British
    Broadcasting Corporation   IV. Series
    823'.914[J]   PZ7

ISBN 0 7278 2093 1

Phototypeset by The Word Factory, Rawtenstall, Lancs,
Printed and bound in Great Britain by
Anchor Brendon Ltd, Tiptree, Essex

To: **YOU**, Chris
From: The Doctor

Chris, may I have a nanosecond of your time? I am about to go on a new space trip. I shall need a new assistant. I have two very able ones. They are standing over me as I type this on my Word Box, er Processor. Have you met them? Peri and Turlough. Peri's a cool young miss. Dresses with flair and thinks with zip. ('Or the other way round,' Peri suggests.) She comes from New England in the US of A. A real Annie Get Your Stungun gal! Turlough, now – he went to school in 'little ol' England'. Good shot with a laser gun. Good man in a tight spot.

My new mission promises to be pretty exciting; so awesome, so terrible, so mind-blowingly earth-shattering (literally!) so – ('Get on with it!' Turlough has just shouted over my shoulder) – er . . . well. . . that I shall need a new assistant.

Peri's asked me to say: THE DOCTOR NEEDS YOU!

WARNING: Before you decide to accept my offer to join the crew of the TARDIS, beware! Are you ready to have a go? Wherever you are in space, whoever you meet? Dare you pit your strength and wits against that Monster of the Milky Way, Garth Hadeez? Dare you look upon the terrible Queen Tyrannica, Garth's devoted and beautiful wife? Not too squeamish to face Garth's master-slaves, the Golons? Could you bear to rub shoulders with the Golons' slave robots, the slimy black Maggots? Could you square up to a Black Hole?

Not put off? Good! Welcome aboard. Step into the TARDIS and begin the adventure of your life with me, the Doctor.

1

The adventure begins innocently enough. This is often the way with the most exciting times of our lives, don't you find, Chris? The Doctor, Peri and Turlough are busying themselves with various tasks about the TARDIS's Control Room. Peri is checking some back-of-an-envelope calculations of the Doctor's – on the micro. 'Just checking!' she tells the Doctor.

'Chris,' the Doctor calls over to you, 'it may only be a routine visit.'

'What may?' you ask.

'The one I'm planning to Mars, Chris.'

'Help you get your space legs,' Peri prattles on. 'Won't it, Turlough?'

'Won't it *what*?' Turlough says irritably. 'Look,

Peri, can't you *see*? I'm listening in on Cyclops.' He points to his headphones.

'Cyclops?' you ask.

'It's a radar thingy,' Peri explains to you quietly so as not to disturb Turlough. 'It scans outer space and can pick up the smallest signal from the farthest planet in the solar system. You see – '

'Sssh!' Turlough whispers. He fiddles with the fine-tuning knob. 'Hey Doctor! Coming through loud and clear!'

You all gather round expectantly. Turlough snaps the headphones off his head. He tears off the printout and leans towards the shredder. 'Sorry,' he says. 'False alarm!' He pops the printout into the shredder's slit mouth.

With lightning speed the Doctor is across the Control Room and his agile fingers save the precious sheet of slot-edged paper.

'Turlough!' the Doctor shouts. 'What *are* you up to?' He turns to you and says apologetically, 'Forgive us, Chris. Always a bit edgy at the start of a trip.' His piercing gaze scans the nearly shredded sheet.

Turlough looks puzzled and says, 'Doctor, I don't know what you're getting so het up about. Only from some alien caller. Some lonesome girl, Anni Hillate it looks like.'

'A *girl*??' the Doctor booms, reading the printout. 'My foot!'

'Oh dear,' Peri says in motherly tones. 'Stubbed our toe, have we?'

'Bless my soul!' Turlough says.

'Not your *sole*, Turlough dear,' Peri says, 'his *foot*.'

'Too big for his boots,' Turlough says under his breath.

'I heard that, Turlough,' the Doctor bawls, 'and the boot is on the other foot!' He waves the printout in Turlough's face.

'This message is nothing less than the most important signal we have ever received from outer space. It's certainly not from a spaced-out, lovelorn lass.'

'Not a lass?' Turlough says softly.

'Alas no!' the Doctor says.

'That's what I said,' Turlough says, even more puzzled now.

'I only wish it were,' the Doctor goes on, prodding the sheet. 'D'you realize what those words spell out?'

'What,' Turlough asks, 'Anni Hillate?'

'ANNIHILATE, Turlough!' the Doctor roars.

'Annihilate me?' Turlough gasps. 'How do they know about *me*, for space sake?'

'Pshaw!' the Doctor splutters. 'Not *you*, Turlough. Just annihilate the solar system. That's all!'

The Doctor quickly absorbs the rest of the message. Turlough had not bothered to read it. He looks up sternly. 'Chris, I didn't exaggerate when I said this would be the most terrifying adventure imaginable. This message is from none other than my hated enemy, Garth Hadeez. He plans to do away with the entire solar system. Not just the world. Oh, no. That's not enough for this Ghengis Khan of the Galaxy. He's marshalled his hideous Golons. Not to mention their robot slaves, the Maggots. If I know anything about this, Queen Tyrannica's behind it.'

'Ghengis Khan! Golons! Maggots! Tyrannica! Wowee!!' you blurt out.

Go to **2.**

2

The Doctor shoots you a kindly look, 'I say, Chris. . . not getting cold feet, are you?' You shake your head. 'Good, good,' the good Doctor says as he plays the Time Console like a cinema organist. He looks up absent-mindedly. 'Chris, you've met Peri, haven't you? And Turlough? Good, good. Welcome aboard.'

Peri explains the rules of the adventure over a cup of Cosmic Coffee. 'You can always call on us for help.'

Turlough chuckles. 'I say, old thing, I wouldn't ask the Doctor to get you out of a scrape if I were you. It could endanger the whole mission. And he never listens, does he, Peri?' He takes a long swig at his cup of Tang, the spacemen's top drink. 'It'd be rotten luck if you made the wrong choice. Then,

I'm very much afraid you'd've had it. In a big way. Just have to begin a new adventure. Still, nothing adventure, nothing gain.'

.'It may turn out differently,' Peri adds soothingly, 'next time round.'

'Done it!' the Doctor whoops. 'Programmed it. For Mars. I have a hunch *that's* where Garth Hadeez is lurking. On the other hand, he *could* be on Halley's Comet.'

Well, Chris, You choose.
*Halley's Comet? Go to **3**.*
*Mars? Go to **4**.*

3

'Halley!' the Doctor exclaims. 'Good choice, Chris. If Garth isn't here, we'll try Mars. Luckily, Halley's small so it won't take a tick to whizz round it and check.'

Halley's Comet being a mere ten kilometres across, the four of you troop round it in next to no time. 'Just a dirty great snowball,' Turlough says.

'No Garth!' the Doctor declares with a snort. He checks his Year Clock. '1607, yeah! On the dot!'

'The year dot?' Turlough asks? 'That's a bit earlier, isn't it?'

The Doctor ignores him, saying, 'If I'm not very much mistaken, Garth Hadeez will be up here soon. Building his new Jerusalem in the Milky Way.'

'When will it be ready?' Peri asks.

'Twentieth century, I'd say,' the Doctor replies. 'Well, chaps, only one thing for it.'

'What's that, Doctor?' you ask.

'Zip down to Earth,' the Doctor says, turning back to the TARDIS. 'Garth has gone to Earth, the old fox!'

You all regain the warmth and comfort of the TARDIS. Once safely inside, the Doctor programs the descent to Earth.

'Touch-down Prague!' the Doctor beams. 'Let's pay a call on Kepler.'

'Who, Doctor?' you ask.

'Only the second scientist ever to understand the solar system, that's who.'

'Oh,' you perk up, 'who was the first? Galileo?'

'Chris!!!' Peri hisses at you, pointing at the Doctor.

The Doctor coughs, modestly, 'Bohemia, here we come! In the year of our Time Lord 1607!'

Go to 5.

4

The TARDIS begins to make the weirdest sound. The others don't seem to notice: they've heard it before. Many times. To you it sounds like a cross between an anchor chain slipping into the sea and a whale wailing out of it. You look startled.

Peri puts a comforting hand on your arm. 'Not to worry, Chris,' she says soothingly.

'Just the TARDIS making landfall,' Turlough explains, quite the old hand.

'Everybody, space suits on!' the Doctor calls out. 'Got everything? Oxygen pack, inter-com, stungun, Swiss Army knife?'

'Inter-coms, Doctor?' you ask. 'What are they?'

'Special coms, Chris,' Turlough says, poker-faced. 'Long-johns. Winter woollies. You know, combinations.'

'Turlough!' the Doctor barks, adding to you, 'Inter-communication gear. Walkie-talkies, y'know, Chris.'

The Doctor flings open the door of the TARDIS. 'There she is. Mars!'

'Cor!' Turlough says in a cockney accent. 'Strike me pink!'

And quite rightly. For not only is Mars itself pink but the sky is, too. Before you stretch craters, plains and huge ice-capped volcanoes. But no sign of life!

'Easy to tell if it's hot or cold up here,' the Doctor says. Is it?

If you think it's hot, go to **41**.
If cold, go to **27**.

5

As the TARDIS soft-lands the Doctor explains: 'I'd like to take a look at the comet from the Earth. And have a look round Prague. My bet is, Garth is somewhere there. First we'll drop in on Kepler, the great stargazer himself. Mother was a witch. And he's squint-eyed. Strange for a stargazer, eh?'

The TARDIS's landing mercifully brings the Doctor's snoozerchat to an abrupt end. You all pile out into Prague on a winter's night in 1607.

'Charming!' you cry. It is a bright cloudless night. The moon lights up the higgledy-piggledy pantomime houses. High gables, walls of scarab green, topaz blue and lemon yellow.

'Bohemia!' the Doctor booms, 'Up there, Gallows Hill. And here, as I thought, Wenceslas Square. Here we are, Number 4. Johannes Kepler's house.'

He leads the way over cobbles and knocks on the heavy wooden door. No answer. He pushes it open. A goat trots out, followed by a couple of hens. Finally, bringing up the rear, appears a tiny hang-dog figure. He is dressed in doublet and hose, with a fine lace ruff round his neck. His beard and moustache makes him look more than his thirty-six years.

'Ah!' he barks, 'you must be the Doctor.'

'I am indeed,' the Doctor smiles and bows in true Bohemian fashion, 'the Time Lord.'

'And I,' the little man curtsies, 'I am Johannes Kepler, the astronomer.'

The Doctor introduces you all. Kepler leads the way into a poky, sombre room. It is littered with papers covered with inky scrawls and a cat sprawling on them. 'I was expecting you,' Kepler says, pointing to an astrolabe and a Zodiac chart. 'I tell fortunes, you see. My horoscope told me.'

'Horror-scope, did you say?' Peri giggles.

'Ha! The horror, you mean,' Kepler growls at her, squint-eyed, and he breaks into song:

'Up above the clouds so high
An evil comet do I spy.
In its tail it nightly revels–
A sign, by Hades, of the Devil's!'

'Hadeez, did you say?' the Doctor asks, 'The very man I'm after.' He touches Kepler's telescope. 'Mind if I take a squint?'

Kepler squints at him doggedly.

'Sorry,' the Doctor apologises. 'I meant a dekko, a butcher's, a peek – as in pekingese!'

Suddenly there is a crash in the corridor of the front door being flung open. Three burly blokes in leather jerkins and kneeboots burst in. They take one look at you all. The leader eyes Peri menacingly.

'That's her!' the leader cries. His two henchmen grab Peri and, before you can say

Swizz Robinson, they have bundled her out into the night.

Kepler shrugs his shoulders. 'Witch-hunters! Hate them. They took my grandmother, you know. . . I blame the comet . . .'

'C'mon, Chris!' the Doctor yells. 'After them!'

Outside the Doctor points up a cobbled street. 'That way, Chris. You keep on their tails. They're making for Gallows Hill, I'll be bound! Turlough and I will head them off at the gibbet.'

Turn to **11.**

6

You step out of the TARDIS. You are on Mars.

'One small step for Chris!' Peri whoops over the inter-com.

'And one giant step for mankind,' the Doctor says, bringing up the rear. 'We're the first men on Mars.'

'Correction!' Turlough calls out anxiously. He points to footprints in the red dust.

'Stay there!' the Doctor says. 'I'll take a look.'

He slithers forward to the lip of the crater, looks down, then waves you all on. Breathlessly, after crawling, you join him. Below you the ground falls away into a gigantic crater. Among the dunes of pink sand in the bowl of the crater stands a giant silver rocket. Round the launch pad seethe a swarm of horrid white maggots with flailing legs, ten on each side of their bodies.

'Ugh!' Peri shrieks. 'Like ants with twenty legs!'

'Centipedes!' you say.

'No,' Turlough laughs. 'Twentypedes! Don't make a sound. Silent as ants!'

'Mutants, actually,' the Doctor says. 'All cloned.'

'That's what I said,' Turlough smiles. 'Silent ants!'

'If I'm not very much mistaken,' the Doctor says, 'they are putting the finishing touches to Garth Hadeez's rocket. He intends to launch, I'd say, a Black Hole into space. Somewhere near Mars if I know anything about our Garth.'

Peri grabs the Doctor's sleeve. 'Doctor, is that him?'

From behind the rocket stands a glowering hulk of a huMANoid. Beside him towers a stunningly beautiful WOMANoid in a regal cloak of royal blue, like a butterfly's wings, edged with glinting knives.

'Yes,' The Doctor nods. 'And that's Queen Tyrannica, next to him.'

Her hair is an unkempt mass of writhing snakes. 'Snakes alive!' Peri hisses, 'wouldn't be her hair-stylist, not if she asped me.'

Suddenly a whole troop of Golons march out of the underground silo beneath the launch pad.

Garth Hadeez raises his right hand in salute. The

Golons return the salute with their right feet, like a chorus line of dancers.

He addresses them in some strange tongue. Turlough aims the long-range bugging device at him. Garth gives out a hideous cacophony of grunts, growls and gurgles at the throat.

The Doctor listens for a second then says briskly: 'It's in Golonic. The demonic form, of course. Turlough, program the Trans-Galactic Babel Master, will you?'

Turlough taps the word GOLONIC into the Babel Master which fits comfortably into the palm of his hand. As he does so, the Doctor tells you: 'Golonic is one of the commonest languages in the Milky Way. In the demonic form the sounds are made in the colon of the stomach. Hence its name.'

'Right-o, Doctor!' Turlough calls. 'Receiving him loud if not too clear.' This is what you hear:

'To each and every Golon
I say to you men, *Roll on
The rocket launch*!
Golons, be staunch!
Into orbit place
A Black Hole in space.
Exterminate the TARDIS!
No matter, men, how hard is
The mighty task ahead
I want the Doctor dead!'

The Golons cheer as one man. Queen Tyrannica claps – with one hand.

'Turlough!' the Doctor booms. 'What on Mars is going on? It's all in rhyme! What mode are you in?'

'Mode, Doctor?' Turlough looks puzzled. 'Mode?. . . Mode?. . . Hah! Got you. *Mode*. For a moment I thought you wanted to know what *mood* I was in.' He peers at the tiny facia of the Trans-Galactic Babel Master. 'Let me see now. . . Ah, *here* it is. . . Oh, sorry, Doctor. Silly me! Had it on RHYME all the time.'

'If you ask me, *more rhyme than reason*,' the Doctor grumbles. 'Well, switch it over to PROSE mode, please Turlough!'

Turlough fiddles with the Babel Master. After struggling with it a bit he gives up.

'The MODE switch, Doctor. It's stuck.'

'Stuck?!' the Doctor booms. 'Well, unstuck it!'

'Oh well, Doctor,' Peri giggles, 'at least a switch in rhyme saves time.'

You and your friends have been so busy nattering you haven't noticed Garth Hadeez. He has spotted you. All the Golons' heads turn as one robot towards you. Garth has ordered them to.

For they *only* obey orders, that's all they *can* do! Garth orders one of his Golons to advance to your side of the crater.

Impetuously you cry, 'I'll fix him, Doctor!' And with a war-whoop you slide down the scree into the bowl of the crater.

'Chris, got your stungun?' Turlough calls after you. 'Release the safety catch!'

You have and you do so. You reach the level. The Golon advances like a robot towards you.

'Me David, you Goloniath!' you cry. But, of course, the Golon doesn't get your merry quip. Garth hasn't ordered him to.

What are you to do?
Throw a die to see what will happen. An odd number means you stun him. Go to **33**.
Throw an even number and you go to **52**.

7

The Doctor calls up some data on Phobos from the micro's Long-Term Memory Store. On its screen it shows these facts:

PHOBOS: Moonlet of Mars.
                Distance from TARDIS: 300 km.
                Diameter: 16 km.
                Gravity: 1/1000 of Earth's gravity.
                Colour: Dark-brown chocolate.

The Doctor makes a rapid check of the read-out from the TARDIS's ET Sensors. Distance. Gravity. Colour. They all check.

'It's Phobos all right!' he says. 'The smallest, darkest, plug-ugliest little moonlet in all the

Milky Way. I think Phobos will pay closer inspection. While I put the TARDIS down on this pock-marked potato of a planet, Chris, keep a sharp look-out for any activity on the surface.'

You adjust the fine-focus control on the radar scan. You watch the screen like a hawk.

The Doctor chunters on from the Control Console. 'Lots of planets have moonlets, you know. Counting out from the Sun there's Venus nil, Earth 1, Mars 2, Jupiter 4.'

'Ah,' Turlough says. 'The League Table. Football, I mean.'

'No!' Peri says. 'The World Series. Baseball.'

'Or,' you throw in, 'a maths series. 0, 1, 2, 4.'

'Kepler thought so, too!' the Doctor says.

'Kepler?' Peri asks.

'Only one of the world's greatest astronomers, Peri,' the Doctor says.

'I'd love to meet him,' Peri says.

'Perhaps we will. . .' the Doctor says meaningfully.

Go to **46.**

The TARDIS lands on Phobos. One by one you step out on this tiny moonlet. The Doctor strides ahead of you in the pink gloom.

'Light's always a pinkish glow on Phobos,' he calls out over his shoulder. 'You see the huge

circle of Mars almost filling the sky? Won't take long to find the blighters, Garth and his crew. You can tell Phobos is tiny from the curved horizon.'

Turlough does a leap for joy. . . and practically disappears from sight!

'Watch it, Turlough!' the Doctor shouts. 'Any more high school high jumps or higher jinks and you'll find yourself really jinxed.'

'Jinxed, Doctor?' Turlough asks.

'Out on your neck. Out in space,' the Doctor explains. 'Gravity is so low here even a grasshopper could put itself into orbit.'

Rounding the next hill of chocolate-coloured sand you spot a rocket lander sitting on its own in a small crater.

Making sure not to jump too high, you and Turlough and Peri make for the lander. Yes, it's Garth's all right. The beggar's on Phobos, for sure.

Suddenly a pink shadow casts a gloom over the three of you. You turn and see Garth Hadeez standing atop a crater, hands on hips, laughing a hideous laugh at you all.

'I challenge you to unarmed combat!' he roars from his height.

'He called me a wombat?!' Turlough fumes.

'No, one-armed combat,' Peri says. 'Which arm? Left or right?'

'Either aim, Plain Jane. I fight with ball and

chain!' Garth roars back. (Of course, the Trans-Galactic Babel Master translates all the speeches from Golonic into rhyming English and the rhymes lead to some misunderstanding.)

'Oh, what a pain!' the Doctor chimes, sighing sadly. 'Suppose I'll have to kill him off.'

'Doctor, Doctor,' you find yourself saying. 'You're far too special to die. I'll fight Garth!'

Going into the fray, Chris? go to **35**. *Running off to draw Garth off? Go to* **21**.

9

You tug on your life-line. Just one small tug's enough and you immediately stop floating along in space. 'Lonely as a clown,' you say to yourself. Another quick tug and in a trice, as sailors used to say when *they* hauled on a rope, you begin wafting back to the TARDIS. Flying through space is so easy you feel you'd outdo even the gibbons at the zoo.

'OK, Turlough!' you call on the inter-com, 'haul in the slack.'

Good old Turlough, you think, as the line gets hauled in. The life-line snakes lazily into the TARDIS. Stout fellow, Turlough. If fact, the stoutest. Nearer and nearer the TARDIS floats.

'Doctor,' you call jokily, 'is the mountain coming to meet Mahomet? Or the other way round?'

'It's all relative, in space,' you hear the Doctor say. 'You're doing nicely for lock-on, Chris. Relatively speaking, as Einstein would say.'

'Whoever he is!' you hear Peri joke.

'Hey, Turlough,' you call out, 'I can read the words POLICE BOX now.' The next moment you are near enough to pick out the smaller letters of the words PUBLIC CALL on the side of the TARDIS. And the next you are safely aboard the phone-box space-and-time ship.

Slipping off your space suit you thank Turlough for hauling you in safely.

'Thank Peri, Chris,' he says. 'She worked the fishing reel. She hauled you in. I simply talked you in.'

'Gee, thanks, Peri,' you gush. 'I think you're marvellous.'

'*Peri*sh the thought!' Peri laughs. 'I think you're *mars*vellous too.'

'Hate to break up the mutual admiration society over there. . . ' The Doctor's voice floats over to you from the other side on the Control Room. 'But I rather fancy the natives are getting restless.'

He jabs an elegant finger at the green radar scan screen.

Turlough joins him in a trice. 'It's only an old snowball, Doctor. By the looks of the smoke coming out of it, it must be on fire.'

'A rocket, I think you'll find,' the Doctor says

gently. 'And, if I'm not very much mistaken, Garth Hadeez's rocket at that.'

Sure enough, Chris, you can see, picked out in green electronic dots on the screen, a white ball with a trail of steam or smoke, you're not absolutely certain.

'Hang about, Doctor!' Peri cries. 'You *sure* it's a rocket?'

'No,' you say, 'that tail is suspiciously long, isn't it? Looks more like a white peacock's tail.'

'*So* it does,' the Doctor says, scratching his head. For once he looks put out, perplexed even. 'I confess,' he confesses sadly, 'unlikely as it may seem to you chaps, who do not enjoy the advantages of being a Time Lord. . . er, where was I?. . . for once I'm. . . well. . . I'm. . . '

'Banjaxed?' you put in.

'Poleaxed?' Turlough chips in.

'Flummoxed?' Peri flings in.

All these suggestions confuse the good Doctor even more than the green image on the radar scan does. While he's pondering such a weighty problem, say what you think the green image could be.
Garth Hadeez's rocket? Then go to 70.
A comet, as Peri suggests? Then go to 53.

10

You quickly work out what 1010 is in ordinary numbers: 10. Simple really. . . when you know how.

Binary's easy: we count in *ones*, *tens* (10s), *hundreds* (10 × 10s) and *thousands* (10 × 10 × 10s). In binary you count in *ones*, *twos* (2s), *fours* (2 × 2s), and *eights* (2 × 2 × 2s). Jot the binary number 1010 under its columns. Set out left to right, it looks like this:

eights	*fours*	*twos*	*ones*
1	0	1	0

And you can see that it stands for 1 *eight* and 1 *two*, which makes ten (10) in our numbers.

You turn the lock ten times to the right. The grill swings open. It looks like an air-vent shaft. Can you slide into it? Yes — with difficulty. You wriggle and squirm your way along it. You come to a vertical shaft. Luckily, it has hand- and foot-holds. You shin up it as quickly as you can. It feels like escaping from a prisoner of war camp. The tunnel levels. Now are you making good time. What's that? A light at the end of the tunnel?

'Not an oncoming train, I hope!' you joke to yourself. No, it's okay. It's an opening. You pop your head out. Ah! It *was* an air vent. The opening gives onto a plain on Phobos. What's more, no Golons! Relief. Phew! You are free.

'Must be holiday-time for Golons,' you think. 'Either that or the day-shift hasn't come on yet.'

Parked on a dune you see a shiny red Rover car. You leap into it, start it up and move off.

Go to **16**.

Gasping for breath you reach Gallows Hill. Low in the sky, Halley's Comet is steaming across the heavens. You drop your eye-line. In the shadows you can just pick out three burly figures doing something round a huge cone of what looks suspiciously like brushwood, sticks and logs.

Suddenly you hear Peri scream with fear. 'I'm not one of the witches of Salem!' she yells. But, of course, the burly men have never heard of Salem.

'That's not for another couple of hundred years,' you think.

'All the same, you'll do!' the leading burly man shouts raucously.

They quickly have Peri tied to a stake on top of the brushwood with stout cords and ropes. Peri screams blue murder until they stop her mouth with a filthy scarf wrenched from round the neck of the smallest of the burly men.

'Blue murder?' the leading heavy cries. 'Nonsense. This is God's work.' He steps to a brazier burning cosily by the tall gallows. He picks up a long wooden torch. He plunges it into the glowing embers of

charcoal. Immediately, the end of the torch blazes into flames with a flickering smoky flare. Sickeningly, it lights up the faces of Peri and of the two assistants, as you suppose they are. All three gather round the huge pile of brushwood.

'Let's see what colour she burns, eh?' the leader chuckles. 'Let's!' his henchmen chime.

'If she burns red, she's a witch. If green, she's innocent.'

'Say, Boss!' one of the henchmen says thickly, 'if she's innocent, won't it be too late to save her?'

'Don't confuse me, Fritz!' the Boss barks out. 'You're blinding me with science as usual. Anyway, perhaps she's colour-blind. Then she won't know.'

'Right, Boss!' Fritz says. *He* knows on which side his bread is buttered.

Fritz shouts, 'Roast the young witch!' The Boss raises the torch on high. Just then the Doctor and Turlough leap out from behind the huge pile of wood about to be Peri's funeral pyre.

What do you do?
Like Micawber see what turns up? Go to **13**.
Go for the Boss? Go to **68**.

12

You lunge back for the dangling rope. It sways dangerously in the biting Martian wind. But you manage to grab hold of it and wind its end round

your waist. Deftly you tie a clove-hitch. You tug on the rope. It begins to rise in jerks. You feel yourself lifted in the air at an incredible speed. As you swing about you feel like a human fly walking up the side of the Empire State Building — though not so safe!

Some Golons have gathered below you. They begin firing at you.

'Rotten shots!' you say into your inter-com.

'Right!' Turlough inter-coms back. 'The Doctor says it's because they only have one eye. Can't judge distance, you see.'

Just then there is another hail of bullets. A whiff of grapeshot! A bit too close for comfort! You kick your legs like an abseiler against the rock, so you swing like a pendulum. 'That should keep 'em guessing!' you hope. Suddenly there is a mighty rumble.

A volley of bullets dislodges an overhanging rock just above you and, luckily, well to your left. This sets off an avalanche of rocks and dust. They crash down on top of the Golons.

You have time to see them flailing on their backs like beetles as you clamber up over the edge of the crater. Turlough hauls you to safety.

'Here, let me give you a hand,' Peri says.

'I've got two, thanks!' you joke, so relieved are you to be safe. 'I say, you two must be strong: it was like going up in a lift — '

'Nothing to it!' Peri blows modestly on her

nails. 'You're as light as a feather, Chris, didn't you know?'

'Am I!' you exclaim.

'Course you are, on Mars.' Peri says. 'A third your weight on Earth. In fact — '

'Cut the chat!' Turlough snaps out. 'Not much time to lose!'

'Or weight!' Peri adds.

Turlough points down into the crater's bowl. Golons are scurrying like ants, making great Martian jumps about the place.

'They're hopping mad!' Peri smirks.

'Per-*ee*!!' Turlough shouts. 'C'mon we must get back to the TARDIS.'

The three of you set off over the red dunes. Over to your right you can just see the friendly blue phone box in the distance. 'Unless it's a mirage,' you think. 'No, on second thoughts, it couldn't be. Not on Mars.' You glance to your left.

'Peri! Turlough!' you puff. 'Look out!'

Over the crater's edge loom half a dozen shiny black ant-like heads, glinting pinkly in the Martian evening glow.

'Run for your life!' Turlough yells. 'As fast as you can!'

And you do. But not fast enough. The going in the soft sand is nightmarishly slow. A vast Goliath-like shadow falls across yours in the red dust ahead of you.

Do you turn and fight? Go to 52.
Trust to luck and your friends to get you out of a fix?
Go to 56.

13

Wise decision, Chris. Congratulate yourself for knowing when you are licked and when to take it easy and sit back.

Turlough leaps forward. As the flames of the Boss's torch are about to lick the wood at Peri's booted feet Turlough reaches for his Swiss Army knife. He snaps it open and produces a cunning miniature fire-extinguisher. With one squirt of white foam he douses the Boss's torch and his hopes of some fun. The Doctor unties the ropes that bind Peri and sets her free.

Turlough's thoroughly enjoyed himself. In fact he turns to you and says: 'For one horrible moment, Chris, I thought you were going to spoil my fun!'

Go to 43.

14

You zip up the hill through a frighteningly windy alley. Suddenly Peri stops.

'What's that?' she says, shivering at your side.

The moon comes out for a second. Above you, you see an old inn sign, swinging in the wind. It shows a werewolf, with one fang dripping gore.

'It's only that old inn sign in the wind,' you say to soothe her. Peri looks up and screams.

'Don't be silly, Peri.' you say. 'It's "Ye Werewolf's Fang" that's all.'

'Well, Chris,' says Peri, 'Which way now?'

Do you go:
Left? Go to **26**.
Right? Go to **55**.

15

Safely back in the TARDIS you tell the Doctor what you think is going to happen. 'So we ought to track Garth, Doctor.'

'Wise decision, Chris,' the Doctor congratulates you. 'You dealt with Garth well: dealt him a nice blow!'

'Doctor!' Turlough calls from the radar scan screen. 'Looks like he's off again. Garth in his module. Into space. Just launching now.' Turlough angles the outside camera by remote control. He picks up a clear picture of Garth's launch module linking up with his command module.

'He has lock-on, Doctor!' Turlough calls. 'Retro rockets firing. Where's he off to, Doctor?'

The Doctor does a quick calculation on the computer then announces: 'My guess is, in orbit round Mars. From the parameters I reckon — '

'Doctor!' Turlough cuts him short. 'UFO in sight!'

Peri peers at the green ball on the screen. 'Hmph! Looks more like a mouldy potato to me!'

'That'll be Mars's other moonlet, Deimos,' the Doctor says. Then he pauses. 'On the other hand it could be. . . the Black Hole. The one Garth is threatening to put into orbit. And where? Round Mars, the devil!!'

'Why round Mars, of all places, Doctor?' Peri asks.

'Why?' the Doctor laughs a little laugh, moving easily to the TARDIS's consol. 'Why? So we'll think it is one of Mars's twin moonlets, that's why!'

'You mean. . . ?' Turlough stammers.

'I do!' the Doctor says grimly. 'Garth's dastardly plan is to hoover us up with that Black Hole of his, soon to be put into orbit. Then nothing'll stop him. He'll stop at nothing. First the TARDIS, then Mars, the Earth, then all the planets!'

'NO?' you just manage to gasp. You can't believe your ears.

'YES!' the Doctor says. 'In short, the whole galaxy, the entire Milky Way goes down the Black Hole. So you see, everyone, this UFO of yours, Turlough, has to be scouted out. Now! Who will volunteer for this mission?'

'ME!' Turlough says gamely.

'Not *me*,' Peri corrects him. 'I.'

The Doctor looks at her sternly. 'No-o, not *you* Peri. Ladies last on this trip.'

'That settles it, Doctor,' you exclaim. 'I'll go.'

You don your space suit and make ready to leave the TARDIS.

'Good luck, Chris!' Peri pats you on the back as you slip into the escape hatch. You step out and begin your space walk. Turlough is in charge of paying out your precious life-line.

Then you see it. Or what you take to be 'it': Garth Hadeez's devilish moonlet, the Black Hole.

Do you approach closer? Go to **23**.
Or do you slip back to the safety of the TARDIS? Go to **9**.

16

The Rover skids through the pink dust. But not to a halt. There is enough 'go' in it to leap gracefully over the chasm and to bounce wildly, like a bucking bronco, on the other side.

A quick step on the gas and the Rover starts roaring up a steady slope. At the top you see, far to the left, the Golons with their lifeless master, Garth Hadeez. You wrench the wheel hard over to the left and do wheelies in the pink dirt, kicking up a fine spray of dust on the off-side.

You think, 'I've a good chance of running the devil down!' And accelerate again. The Rover responds beautifully. You think, 'Garth must have some fine technologists working for him. It's as good as a Beach Buggy.'

'Yippee!' you yell in the windless, airless space of Phobos.

Suddenly the Rover lurches. The engine dies on you. And you are rolling towards the Golons. Help! What now?

The Doctor comes through on the inter-com. 'It's OK, Chris. If you're really pushed, you can do a Time Slip. Or you can leap out and make for that nearby cave. I've got you covered on the radar scan in the TARDIS.'

Which is it to be, Chris?
A Time Slip (back four hundred years, in fact)?
Then go back to 5 and join the Doctor in the TARDIS.
Or cut and run? Go to 61.

17

You advance. Garth stands his ground. He looks magnificent, terrifying, supreme. A super-Rambo hulk of a creature. A giant Cyclops with his one red, gleaming eye. Its glance pierces your very skin. Suddenly he falls on one knee.

You step forward. 'I'll crush you with one blow of my Earthling fist!' you shout. But it is a trick.

Too late you hear the Doctor on the inter-com: 'Behind you, Chris!'

You feel something slimy on the back of your neck. Like a black octopus tentacle, it whips

round your windpipe. It threatens to suffocate you. Next to your face you see that of a Maggot!

A Golon, standing by, pulls it off you — at Garth's orders. He wants you alive, not dead. Didn't think you'd be pleased to see a Golon, did you? Saved in the neck, er nick of time!

Acting under orders the Golon lifts you like a cushion. He carries you under his plastic black arm. He marches you of to the rocket silo. You go down in a lift, along a concrete corridor. He throws you into a bunker and slams the door on you. KLANG!

It is pitch dark. What are you going to do? Go to **42**.

18

You leap out of the Rover. The Golons spot you. Some of them peel off from the group carrying Garth to the rocket lander.

You run for a cave in the steep side of the crater. Once inside, you get your breath back and peer out. The Golons are approaching fast. Too fast for you to escape and make a run for it now.

You back into the cave. At the entrance you can see several Golons outlined in the pink glow of Mars's great red disc. They begin to advance on you. Strangely, though, they seem lost, without purpose. They mill about but don't really close in on you as you'd expected.

'Got it!' you say to yourself. 'They aren't

programmed to think for themselves. And Garth hasn't given them any specific orders. Perhaps all he said was "After him!" Something like that.'

You try an experiment. You throw a rock up at the far end of the cave. There is a tremendous fall of rock. It buries some of the Golons. But they don't seem to mind. So you run through them like a rat through over-fed cats. And you gain the comparative freedom of the cave mouth.

By now the Golons have lifted Garth's hulking great form into the front seat of the Rover. Even from this distance, you can see he comes to. He switches on the engine. And, wouldn't you know, it coughs into life and he drives off into the sunset, er Mars-set.

You wend your way back to the TARDIS.

Go back to **15**.

19

You run in leaps and bounds after the Rover conveying Garth. . . where? He hasn't seen you so the Golons aren't too sure what to do about you. As you follow it through craters — easy enough to follow the wheel marks — you soon find you are miles from the TARDIS.

Suddenly the sky goes bright red against the pinkish glow of Mars. As you breast the brow of the next crater you are in time to see a rocket lander taking off. It's Garth, shooting off into space.

Bad luck, Chris. You failed to catch the devilish Garth. So that's the end of this adventure. Don't worry. The Doctor won't leave you to die on Phobos. Hardly have you seen the last of Garth and his rocket than the TARDIS settles into the soft dust next to you. And the Doctor welcomes you aboard 'For another adventure'.

The Golons? Well, they're just as happy to die in the service of their Overlord Garth Hadeez on Phobos as anywhere else.

THE END

20

You lead the way down a dark alleyway. The overhanging gables of the houses on either side of the alley are so close, opposite neighbours can shake hands. The gables almost blot out the bright streamer tail of the comet. You and Peri creep like white mice. You both hug the rough lath and plaster walls.

'What's that?' Peri hisses in your ear.

'What?' you hiss back.

'That shadow, Chris. In the doorway.'

'Which doorway. We've passed lots.'

By now your heart is going like a steam-hammer, tapocketa-pocketa-*pock*.

'Chris, the alley's getting wider.'

'As long as it's not getting any fatter, Peri! Sorry, just my gallows humour. Hey! You're not wrong. We're coming to a square.'

No answer.

'Peri!'

You whip round. No Peri! Where is she? Must've slipped into a doorway a few doors back. You retrace your steps. You feel into the dark doorways. Tapocketa-pocketa-POCK.

There is a sudden shriek. It sounds like Peri's voice — *heavily* muffled. Has she fallen into the hands of the heavies? Oh no! Which doorway did it come from, her shriek? Then you see it — a flicker of candlelight through a crack in a rickety clapboard door. You gingerly push the door open.

It creaks loudly on its rusty hinge. So far so good, you inwardly sigh. Suddenly a rough grimy hand grabs your wrist. Uh-uh! Not so good.

The next thing you feel is yourself being hurled bodily through the air. Fortunately you land on a pile of straw in the corner of a little room. It is lit by a single candle. Its flame gutters in the draught, throwing up terrifying shadows on the roughcast walls. And there is Peri. She is struggling in the hands of the Boss.

He manhandles Peri and grins, toothlessly: 'C'mon, Fritz. Show our guest who's a ghost. She ain't got the ghost of a chance, 'as she? Heh, Heh!'

He laughs so much he nearly chokes himself, coughing and spluttering.

'Nasty cough you've got on your chest, Boss,' Fritz simpers.

'On my jest, did you say, Fritz?' The Boss roars with laughter at his little jape. Then he looks evil and serious. 'Tie our guest up, Hans.'

Hans shambles towards you in your corner. Seconds out of the ring, you think. Underneath the straw you feel something metallic. Your left hand closes on it, Your right hand reaches into your pocket for your Swiss Army knife.

What's your next move, Chris?
Pull a fast one on Hans with your Swiss Army knife? Go to **40**.
Create a diversion with the metal thingy? Go to **32**.

21

You leap over the brow of the crater. A mere couple of hundred metres! Nothing to it on Phobos. There the team of Golons are, lugging their unconscious leader Garth around. They don't know what to do, for he is not able to give them orders. When a Golon says 'We only obey orders' — like some other black-shirted nasties you can think of, Chris! — they mean they ONLY obey orders. They can't do anything else!! For they are nothing but Garth's robot slave race of superhulks. Now's your chance, Chris.

Win glory and perhaps, who knows, a nod of approval from the Doctor? Heaven! But discretion is the better part of Valhalla. You can't tackle that rabble of Rambos on your own. Should you get back to the Doctor? No, press on regardless. You race up to the top of the next crater and there, sitting in the pink Martian glow of evening — the days are incredibly short on Phobos, as you know — is nothing other than. . .

Garth's Rover, his 'Beach Buggy' car for roving round planets.

'Wowee!' you whoop. And leap into the driving seat. Luckily, Garth has left the keys in the ignition. A quick flick of the wrist and, VROOM-VROOM, it starts first time. You grasp the gear lever, throw it into 'Overdrive' and away you zoom.

Up a slight rise in the pink dust and ahead you see a chasm. What do you do?

Step on it! Go to **54**.
Slam into reverse. Go to **36**.

22

You dive for cover behind the dune. You peer round the rock. The Golons are advancing with caution. You sit back to consider your options. You feel a rope dangling by your head. How on Earth — Mars rather — has Turlough managed to swing it all the way out to the dune?

No, it isn't a rope. It's a tentacle of a black Maggot. Before you know where you are, you are smothered by a swarm of nibbling Maggots.

That's the end of this adventure. Go back to **2** *and begin a new one, Chris.*

23

Rotten luck, Chris! It's definitely Garth Hadeez's terrifying invention: the hellish artificial Black Hole. Down you go, Chris, *spaghettified*!

So that, sadly, is that. The end of this adventure. So try another one.

THE END

24

'Manners, you little toad!' she cackles. . . and turns you into one. Bad luck, Chris! Not to worry: happens all the time in Ye Olde Prague. You apologize.

'Oh, that's toadily different,' she croaks and turns you back into YOU again.

Now you may go to **39** *and consider your options again. TAKE CARE, Chris!*

25

You both turn your steps right. Peri looks up at a wooden street sign, nailed to the wall. Kafka Lane.

'We're on course for the castle, Chris!' she cries triumphantly.

At the top of the lane the castle looms up before you. A deep moat surrounds it. But the drawbridge is down. You scamper across its heavy planks and arrive at a thick oak door, studded with huge iron nails. You bang on the door with your fists. You hear slow, dragging footsteps inside. Through a slit window next to the door you spy a chink of candlelight. There is a rattling of heavy chains. A bolt is drawn back. A key turns in the rusty lock. The great door creaks open.

There stands a huge thickset figure in a monk's cowl and hood which conceals his face. All you can glimpse is a single gleaming eye, glinting under the hood.

'He's as thick as the door!' Peri whispers to you.
'Thicker!' you hiss back.

The figure beckons you in. It leads the way to a vast archway, covered with a heavy curtain of carpet. The door slams behind you. You turn. There Turlough stands beside an empty knight in armour. He steps out to join you on tip-toe. The monk, ahead of you, does not notice.

Go to **44.**

26

You swing left round the corner of 'Ye Werewolf's Fang' Inn.

'Who'd want to go and drink in there?' Peri says to you, quickening her pace to get away from the place.

'People who like drinking Bull's Blood!' you laugh.

'Bull's Blood?!' Peri says. 'Yuk!'

'Yes, it's a real drink, Peri. Hungarian.'

You put what feels like a league between you and the probably charming hostelry. The lane winds and twists so much you quite lose your sense of place or direction. But you both hasten on.

'Peri, you *sure* the witch told us to bear *left* at "Ye Werewolf's Fang"?'

'Well, Chris, it certainly wasn't right at the werebear's ear!' Peri laughs. Then she bleats, 'Oh dash! It's come on to rain.'

The moon briefly shines through a sudden gap in the scudding clouds. You stare at Peri's face aghast.

'Peri! What *have* you done?'

She has a streak of blood on her cheek. She stops like a rabbit. You look up. Above you both slowly swings in the gusty wind a newly strung-up corpse. He is hanging from a gibbet. Obviously his blood has dripped down and splashed Peri. But you decide not to alarm her unduly. You merely whistle the 'Eton Boating Song',

'Swing, swing, together
Jolly good hanging weather. . . '

You point to the gibbet, and ask: 'Which way now?'

With remarkable calmness Peri puckers her lips and asks in her New England drawl, 'Say Chris, do we hang a left or a right here?'

'Looks more like a thief!' you say.

Which way do you go?
Left? Go to **62**.
Right? Go to **65**.
Straight on? Go to **30**.

27

Yes, it's always cold on the Red Planet. It's also got a very thin atmosphere of carbon dioxide, the gas in the bubbles of a fizzy drink. Cheers!

Go back to **6**.

28

'Tell me, witches!' you say (rather rudely), 'the way to the castle!'

'Witches!' the crones screech. 'You durst call us *witches*?'

Peri steps in gallantly to smooth things over. 'I think you misheard, my dear ladies. What my friend said was, 'Tell me, which is the way to the castle? By the way, I'm Peri.'

'Oh, that's different,' the toads crone says with a grim grin. The natterjacks hag crosses herself. 'Do you *have* to go, my friends? Don't you know what day it is?'

'Day?' Peri shakes her head.

'It's St Ferocity's Eve tonight!' the natterjacks hag says. At her dread words the happy roisterers fall silent.

'When the clock strikes midnight — '

'On the stroke of twelve,' Mistress Natterjacks adds.

'Graveyards yawn,' Mistress Toads croaks, 'Vampires roam. And the evil One walks. It has power to kill you.'

'Assuredly,' Mistress Natterjacks adds. 'It will slay you!'

'Will it?' you say. 'Can't see the funny side of it myself.'

'Please tell us the way,' Peri pleads.

'Not without the magic words!' Mistress Toads says.

'Here's a florin,' you say, flipping her a Bohemian coin.

'Those *are* the magic words,' she says. Then she chants in a strangely American accent, Peri notes:

'Has my harangue
A New World twang?
'Tis to make merry
Our young friend Peri.
Like Jack and Jill
Go up the hill.
At "Ye Werewolf's Fang"
A left you hang.
Don't let gibbet
Your way inhibit.
But at the stake
A right you take.
Then the Castle gain
By Kafka Lane.'

'Gee, thanks a zillion!' Peri gushes at the crone. She bends down and pats one of the toads. The toad begins croaking happily up at Peri.

'Oh, yes, thanks.' You remember your manners.

'Say no more!' the crone says modestly. The toad instantly stops croaking.

'Got that, Peri?' you ask. Peri nods and you set off at a brisk trot up the hill.

As you go, the crone shouts after you,

'To be explicit,
You cannot miss it!'

Go to **14.**

29

The Doctor calls out to Garth over the Babel Master:

'See you in an hour
When you'll feel our
Might and main —
Thanks to your ball and chain!'

'That'll fox him,' the Doctor chuckles.

'I didn't get you, Doctor,' you say, as you make a thousand-metre leap to join him and the others.

The Doctor explains on the way back to the TARDIS. 'You see, Chris, that spiked ball is now in orbit round Phobos. In an hour it will. . . well, you'll see. Trust me!'

After a half-time cup of Tang you all troop out to

the pitch, that is, the plain. Garth has already taken up his original position. Nearby his faithful Golons are standing in a solid phalanx.

You spot a dot on the horizon — the horizon of Phobos, that is. It seems absurdly close, like a highish hill in rolling countryside. Even as you think this, the spot becomes a dot. And then a blot. And finally a shot. The dot becomes the shot Garth Hadeez's whirled at you in about fifteen seconds flat.

SLAP! BANG! POW! KERANGGGGGG!!!

The ball thuds into Garth Hadeez's head from behind. He doesn't know what's hit him. He crashes like a demolished tower block into the pink rubble. For once his Golons pretty well know what to do. In a mere matter of a minute they decide to lurch forward. They lift their leader shoulder high. They carry him off the field of battle. They carry off this job well: after all they spent years at school learning how.

Do you feel like giving chase? Go back to **21**.
Discretion the better part of valour, eh, Chris? Then go to **66**.

30

'Right on, Chris!'
    'Right, Peri!'
    'NO, Chris! Not right, right *on*. Check?'
    'Sorry, Peri. Forgot you were an American. *Check!*'

'I most certainly am *not* Czech, Chris. I'm from New England. Yes indeedy, I am. Check?

'If you say so,' you say diplomatically. And you lead the way along the dark winding alley.

An eerie growl stops you dead in your tracks. Peri grabs your arm and stammers, 'Wha-wha-what's thaaat, Chris?'

'Oh, only a werebear, Peri.'

'Ugh! Chris, how awful!'

'Ghastly.'

'G-g-g-grisly!'

'No, Peri.' You put your arm round her shoulders.

'What's that?' Peri starts. 'Bear right?'

'Barely!' you laugh. So pleased are you with your pun, you don't look where you are going and bump into a post carelessly left stuck in the middle of the cobbled way.

'Ouch!' You rub your poor shoulder. 'Stupid thing to leave in the middle of the road.'

'Drunk again!' Peri calls to you, to keep up your flagging spirits. She rubs your bruised arm. 'Know what you are, Chris?'

'Bruised!' you say.

'No, Chris, PUN-ch drunk!'

You groan — but not from the bump!

Peri taps the post. 'What's this, Chris?'

You walk round the thing you 'went bump into in the night'. 'Gosh!' you gasp. 'It's a stake!'

'Well done!' Peri congratulates you.

'I don't know if the steak is well done, Peri,' you say. 'But the witches tied to it would be. Like a Steak Tartare.'

'I'm off! Peri yells. 'I don't want to go to the stake and be burnt to a frazzle again, thank you! Good-bye, stake!'

'Steak, ta-ta!' you wave to it.

Well, Chris, which way to the castle now?
Do you go:
Left? Go back to 25.
Right? Go to 63.

31

You step out of the TARDIS. And you see nothing but a polar wasteland. But it's not like the poles on Earth: no ice floes, no penguins, no polar bears. Instead across the ice dunes a wonderful sight meets your gaze: a glistening, silver city of steel and ice. All giant igloos of steel, chromium domes and ice-blue rockets.

'So!' the Doctor exclaims, '*This* is where Garth Hadeez has been all my life. Halley's Comet. Well, since 1910, anyway.'

'Why 1910, Doctor?' Peri asks.

'That was the date of the last fly-past of Halley's Comet. In this neck of the Milky Way.'

'Wowee!' you whoop and make to run forward. The Doctor grasps your arm. 'Watch your steps, Chris! I smell danger.'

'Just a quick recce, Doctor!' you shout and run to a huge cave in the side of an ice dune.

'Come back, Chris! the Doctor calls out. 'It may be a trap. Make sure there are no Golons in there!'

You peer inside. You turn, cup your hands and hulloo back to the Doctor very distinctly: 'O. Kay! Emp-ty!'

'Tsk!' the Doctor tutses. 'That spells *danger* to me.'

'Sorry, Doctor,' Turlough says in a puzzled voice. 'How does O-K-M-T spell DANGER?'

'I hardly think this is the time to discuss spelling, Turlough!' the Doctor says.

Just then a noise like a badly oiled chain-saw brings you up short.

'Spell, did you say?' The words hit you like an arctic blast. 'I can do spells!'

You turn, trembling, to see, stepping out of the cave the majestic form of the icy Queen Tyrannica. She towers over you and glowers down at you. She is dressed, you note, in her royal blue cloak, prettily edged with sharp knives. She keeps her hair-do of serpents warm under a plastic bubble like an airport phone booth.

Your thoughts are cut short by her pointing a six-inch nail — on the end of her finger — at you and rasping: 'What's your name? *You?*'

Turlough bellows, 'Don't tell her, Chris!'

She hisses like her writhing snakes. They strike you as giving her hair a stylish permanent wave.

Her chain-saw voice cuts through the icy air as she casts a spell in Golonic upon you. Luckily, Turlough's Trans-Galactic Babel Master gives a simultaneous translation. He shouts the results at you.

'Now listen to this,
Hear my spell, young Chris.
I forecast you'll do or die!
But first cast once a die.
Throw a 5 or 6
And live to play more tricks.
But throw a 1 or 2, *or*
What's as dreaded,
A 3 or 4
And you are deaded!
Now you know your fate,
Let the die *de*-cide it, mate!'

If you throw a 1, 2, 3 or 4 your adventure is over.
If you throw a 5 or 6, go to **60**.

32

You grip the metal thing under the straw more tightly as Hans advances on you like a tired juggernaut. Your fingers can dinstinctly feel the shape of the thing. It's curved and has holes along its length. It's a horseshoe — a lucky one!

'Watch out!' you yell, nodding at the doorway. Hans turns his head to watch out for a moment —

well, quite a longish moment actually, for he is a bear of a man with very little brain. You yank the horseshoe out of the straw and hurl it at Fritz. He ducks and it hits the Boss, who rounds on Fritz. He lets go of Peri and lands a socking great punch on Fritz's jaw. Fritz doesn't know what has hit him. He looks dazed. In the confusion Peri escapes from the room into the alleyway, banging the front door behind her.

'After her!' the Boss yells.

Fritz and Hans lumber woodenly down the corridor. You hear them go through the front door — with a rending crash of wood. In their haste they forgot to open it, you guess.

It's between you and the Boss now. You draw your ace from up your sleeve — or rather your Swiss Army knife from your pocket. The Boss takes one look at it and shouts 'Ghosts alive!' He beats it. You hear his clod-hoppers crashing down the cobbles outside and into the distance.

You step outside through the splintered cut-out Fritz and Hans obligingly left in the door. You find Peri. She has been hiding in the next doorway, waiting for you.

Go to **39**.

Your stungun stuns the Golon. He crashes to the ground, sending up a spray of fine red dust. The Queen points her talons at another Golon. He surges into action. He begins to move towards you, in great 10-metre leaps and bounds.

'Doctor!' you call frantically over the inter-com. 'What shall I do?'

The Doctor's voice comes back to you, calm and firm: 'Don't, whatever you do, Chris, try to go back this way. That Golon fellow will catch you up on the slippery slope. Run along the dried-up river bed!'

You look down. Sure enough, there is a long hair-crack in the sandy ground. You begin haring along it. To your joy, you find you can run in giant leaps, like the Golon. You look up to the top of the crater. There are Peri and Turlough, running like billio round the crater's edge to meet you, as you pant across the crater's diameter.

You look round for a breathless second. The giant Golon is still on your heels. Worse, he's catching up on you! Your legs feel like liquid lead. You are ready to drop. Suddenly you hear an ear-splitting roar. It's right behind you! Your last hour has come, Chris. . .

You dare to look round for one last look. Hey! The Golon has gone. Vanished into thin air! But how?

As if in answer to your unspoken question,

Turlough's cheery voice crackles in your headphones. 'OK, Chris. Ease off now! Sorry about the delay. Stungun trouble. Safety catch stuck. Managed to pick him off all the same. Meet you above the end of the river bed. Over and out!'

There is a click. You are on your own again. You settle into the steady pace of a long-distance runner. 'Boring!' you begin to think when a spurt of red dust kicks up by your feet.

'Hell's bells! Someone or something's taking a pot-shot at me!' you think. You start zig-zagging about, like a hunted hare. The Golons' pot-shots are spitting up dust left and right of you. You leap out of the way, always just in time.

The slope is getting steeper. Your pace slows to a walk. Your feet sink in the red sand. The going's really slow. You think, 'Gosh! I'm a walking target. In another nanosecond I'll be a sitting one! Evasive action called for, Chris!'

As luck has it (sometimes!) you spot a low dune running out from the crater's cliff-face. Yes, you can take cover behind that. If only you can get to it in one piece.

You make a run for it, Army-crouch style. Then Turlough, from on top of the crater, calls you up: 'Rope coming down, Chris!'

What do you do?
Run back to the rope? Go to **12**.
Make a dash for the dune? Go to **22**.

'Genius!' The Doctor beams at Peri. 'And you, Chris. Peri's answer sounded a bit soppy, didn't it? She was having you on. Yes, sunlight really *does* push the specks of dust in the comet's tail away from the Sun.'

'I read somewhere, Doctor,' Turlough says, 'that space scientists are planning to drive space-ships by light beams.'

'Right, Turlough,' the Doctor says. 'Can't think why they haven't asked me about it. I'd've got it off the ground for them by now!'

'Nice one, Doctor!' Peri laughs. But the Doctor doesn't see his own joke.

'This is not a comedy, Peri!' he says sternly.

'More comety than comedy, wouldn't you say, Doctor?' Peri says.

The Doctor goes on: 'The head of the comet is nothing but a dirty great snowball with a great white hairy streamer for a tail. About ten kilometres across. About the size of Phobos, in fact.'

The Doctor's snoozer-speech is cut short by a sudden hail of blows on the TARDIS's door.

'Don't open it!' the Doctor snaps. 'Any of you!'

He steps smartly to the Control Console, flicks several switches in quick succession, does a lightning calculation on the micro, and looks up triumphantly. 'It's as I feared, my friends. We seem to be about sixty million kilometres off course. The hail of blows on the door is from dust in the tail of Halley's Comet!'

'Halley-lujah!' Turlough and Peri chorus.

'Really!' the Doctor says mock sternly. 'You two! Too much for me to handle!'

'Oh, I rather go for Handel, Doctor.' Turlough says. 'Smashing composer.'

'Turlough!' the Doctor barks. 'Pull yourself together!'

'Why,' Peri smiles sweetly, 'is he coming apart?'

'Right, chaps.' the Doctor announces. 'We're going in. I'm putting the TARDIS down. On the comet's head.'

As the TARDIS makes the descent the Doctor says in a puzzled voice: 'Can't think how we got into the tail of Halley's Comet. I promise you, I didn't plan it.'

'Of course,' Peri says soothingly, 'it's a comet, not a planet.'

Go to **31**.

35

'Oh, do you think so, Chris?' the Doctor says modestly. 'I suppose I am fairly valuable, now you mention it. Well, look, if you're going into the fray for us, take a tip from me. I ran a little program on the micro this morning, I bunged in all the known facts about Phobos. Came up with some amazing facts. F'rinstance, if you hit a cricket ball with a bat — '

Garth Hadeez's grating voice cuts the Doctor off mid-speech. Over the Babel Master you hear:

'Though I'm hellishly cruel,
I challenge you to a duel.
Choose your weapons!
As it heppens
Mine, I make plain,
Is ball and chain.'

'Tsk, tsk.' The Doctor frowns at Turlough. 'Turlough, I do wish you'd get that *Burble* Master fixed. It sounds ridiculous in rhyme.'

'Sorry, Doc — er, Doctor,' Turlough says contritely.

'A stick in time,' Peri trills, 'makes it rhyme.'

'Something useful you *can* do, Turlough,' the Doctor says, 'Nip back to the TARDIS and get your tungsten cricket bat. Be a good fellow and move those stumps.'

'Stumps. Bat.' Turlough chuckles. 'That's good, Doctor. Didn't know you played cricket.' With that, Turlough jumps to it, and the TARDIS. In a couple of giant leaps he's there — no great feat on Phobos, mark you. A couple more and he is back with his tungsten bat.

'Here you are, Chris,' he puffs, offering you his bat. 'Knock anything for six with this.'

Now's your chance to prove yourself, Chris.

You step forward and shout, via the Babel Master, at Garth:

> 'A duel, Hadeez, I accept.
> At bat and ball I'm more adept
> Than, I must explain,
> At ball and chain.'

'Oh, Chris,' the Doctor calls to you. 'Get Garth to agree to fight on the high plain since you agree to his deadly ball and chain.'

Garth Hadeez accedes to your request. He is in the giving vein today. The pair of you move to a high plateau above the crater. From nowhere a team of ghastly Golons appear, eager to see some Golonic fun.

You look round. The Doctor waves an encouraging hand at you. He cheers you on — by mistake through the Babel Master which naturally turns his words into rhyme:

> 'Don't be Golonic.
> Ya gotta be bright,
> Dear Chris.
> It'd be moronic
> To lose a fight
> Like this.
> Just do as I say
> And you'll be OK. Don't miss!'

You face the Goliath-like Garth. He whirls a horrid-looking spiked ball at the end of a black chain round and round his head, like a Scots shot-putter. He lets it go. It comes hurtling at you as, over the inter-com, the Doctor's voice calls calmly: 'Duck, Chris! Give it a late cut. Just a tap, mind. Don't want to send it into space! Just into orbit.'

You do just as the Doctor orders. You duck, tip the spiked ball with Turlough's tungsten bat. There is some clapping from the pavilion, er the bleachers, er, the trio.

Peri twangs, 'Move over, Babe Ruth, er Joe di Maggio!'

Turlough cheers, 'Eat your heart out, Ian Botham!'

'Here Chris comes!' they both add.

'Tea-time!' the Doctor calls.

Garth explodes with rage. He roars, 'That's not cricket!'

'Well, you can stick it — ' Turlough begins to say. But the Doctor cuts in quickly with: 'We'd like to consider our options.'

Do you go back to the Doctor? Then go to 29.
Or run for cover? Go to 17.

36

You slam the gear into reverse. Then back away from the chasm. You turn so that you hug the edge of the chasm. You peer round eagerly. No signs of danger. But no sign of the TARDIS either.

Now what?

No need to panic. Remember where the red circle of Mars was? Keep it on the same side of you and eventually you should come to the TARDIS. Sure enough, you see the friendly blue phone box across a couple more dunes.

You step on it and the Rover takes off. Help! Are you going into orbit? No. Relief! The Rover makes a perfect four-point landing outside the TARDIS. You skid to a halt, leap out and bang on the door.

Turlough lets you in with a cheery, 'We were just wondering where you'd got to. Welcome aboard!'

Go to **15**.

37

Sorry, Chris. Turlough called your bluff. But don't be down-hearted. It was a jolly good guess. You'll be glad to know the great scientist Sir Isaac Newton thought like Turlough. Great minds think alike!. . . Well, sometimes. But they both happen to be wrong.
Go to **53** *and choose again.*

38

That's right! Sorry, left is correct. Go to **30**.

'After them!' you cry.

'Hang about, Chris!' Peri cries. She puts a restraining hand on your arm. 'The Doctor's calling.'

You both listen to the familiar crackle of the Doctor's voice coming from the walkie-talkie Peri keeps on the lapel of her plum-red velvet jacket. It makes her feel like a medical Doctor: not a Time Lord, though.

'Peri! Chris! Forget about tailing the Boss and his ghostly ghouls. I've tracked down Garth Hadeez!'

'Say, jeez!' Peri cries.

'No, no,' the Doctor's voice comes over a shade tetchy on the walkie-talkie. 'Not "Say cheese!" I said "Hadeez". I'll spell it: H–A–D–E–E–Z. He's somewhere in Prague Castle. He's got poor Kepler prisoner. Getting him to work out the comet's orbit for him, the rotter! Roger, over-and-out!'

'Who's Roger? you ask.

'Oh, that's what you say when you sign off,' Peri explains. The pair of you make your way down the dark alley into a market square. It is thronged with merry, roistering peasants who, for the moment, have managed to forget the ill-omened comet whizzing over their heads.

'Which way to the castle?' Peri asks.

'Look!' you say, pointing to a couple of old crones, sitting beside a basket. 'One of those witches is sure to know.'

One of them is crying, 'Buy my toads and natterjacks! Lucky charms against yucky harms! Ward against comets the night sky vomits!'

You step up to them. One of them eyes you slyly and whines, 'Care for a nice young toad, sir?'

And the other chimes in with, 'Or a good old natterjack?'

Do you cheekily reply, 'No time for a natter, thanks and, by the way, my name's not Jack?' Then go to **24**.

Or do you politely ask them the way to the castle? Go to **28**.

40

It's now or never. You *must* save Peri from the perils of Peri. She is in Boss's hands which are still dangerously tight round her neck. Your hand reaches for your Swiss Army knife. Before Fritz or Hans can do a thing, you have drawn it. They take one look at the knife and together, yell:

'I don't want to be turned into a ghost!'

And they rush headlong from the dingy room, down the dingy corridor, and through the front door. You hear a shuddering crash and the sound of splintering wood. In your best Humphrey Bogart voice you call after them, 'Next time, kiddos, try opening it first!'

'Any more funny tricks,' the Boss snarls, 'and she gets it. In the neck. Hands up!'

You put your hands up, the Swiss Army knife still clutched in one fist. With your foot you deftly feel for the heavy metal thing in the straw. With a neat flick of your ankle you kick it into the air. The Boss takes his eye off you for a second. This gives you enough time with one hand — single-handedly, that is — to open the Swiss Army knife. Like a Space Age toy it opens out into a robotic replica of Garth Hadeez.

The Boss takes one look at this miniature model of his Master and falls to his knees, blubbering for mercy.

'Get up,' you say coolly, 'and get out! And don't show your ugly mug round here again. If you know what's good for you.'

The Boss scurries off. You hear his clothes tear as they catch on the splinters left in the clapboard front door.

Peri rushes to you. She throws her arms round you and hugs you.

'Thanks, Chris! You saved my life!'

'It was nothing, kiddo!' you smirk modestly. And the pair of you sally forth into the alleys of Prague.

'We must find the Doctor and warn him about the men,' Peri says.

Go to **39**.

41

No, Chris. Mars is cold. The ice-capped volcanoes were a bit of a clue. Though, of course, volcanoes on the Equator (on Earth!) are snow-capped. Because Mars is freezing cold, there is no life on it.
Go back to 4 and consider your options again.

42

You pull out your Swiss Army knife and flick open its portable torch. You aim its beam all round the bunker. Then you see it, a small grille halfway up the wall. You peer closely at it. It has a combination lock on it. If only you could open it! It's just big enough to wriggle through. Hang on, Chris. What's that, scratched on the metal surround? A letter and some numbers. R 1010. Surely you don't turn the knob a thousand and ten times to the right. Ah! perhaps it's not in ordinary counting numbers. Could it be. . . in binary? Then you'd know the combination.

Turn to 10 with the combination number written in ordinary numbers and see if you're right.

43

Turlough puts out the flames and sees you're all safe. Then he turns his attention to the heavies. He gives the Boss himself a thorough squirt with the mini fire-extinguisher. Then he swivels round and squirts the other two. All three are now covered in white foam.

'Three squirts for three squirts!' Turlough yaroos.

The heaviest heavy, the Boss, staggers back. 'I'm staggered! Look at you. Fritz! Hans! *Look* at you both! You're *ghosts!*'

'Speak for yourself, Boss!' Hans blusters.

'He's turned you into. . . into. . . ' Fritz blurts out.

'In TWO??!' the Boss shrieks. 'You mean I'm *twins?*' He grasps poor Fritz by his jerkin. 'You're not seeing double, are you? You drunk or sumpink?'

'We. . . we. . . we're *all* ghosts, Boss,' Hans stammers.

The Boss grabs Hans by the ears and shakes him. 'Is she a witch?' he roars.

Hans's ox-like brain crumbles. 'How can she be, Boss?' he blubbers. 'She didn't burn. And only witches burn.'

'Why, you dumb ox,' the Boss fumes, 'because she can do magic. Run for your life, men! I must tell Garth!'

The three heavies take to their heels and hob-nail down the cobbled street.

'Hear that?' the Doctor asks. 'Garth Hadeez. He's lurking somewhere about.'

'It certainly lurks like it.' Turlough says, with a smile.

'Yes,' the Doctor says, 'he's here now.'

'*Now?*' Peri says. 'Surely you mean *then*, Doctor? It's 1607.'

'Seven minutes past four?' Turlough exclaims. 'Gracious, tea-time already!'

'My hunch, for what it's worth, is this,' the Doctor says, ignoring Turlough's funny.'Even now, I suspect, Garth Hadeez is busily building his city in the sky. On Halley's Comet. When we last saw it, four hundred years later, it was finished, you remember. But if we catch him now, his defences will be down. The hunt for Garth Hadeez is on, chaps. Fan out everybody. Comb the city. Explore every avenue. Leave no cobble unturned. We must get Garth before he gets up to the comet and his tricks again.'

The Doctor and Turlough slip off stealthily. Meanwhile you, Chris, and Peri mosey off another way, singing softly to yourselves:

'We seek him here,
We seek him there,
That demm'd elusive Hadeez man
Whom no one can be tougher than.'

Go to **20**.
Hey, hang about Chris! Perhaps you'd rather go with Turlough and have the Doctor take Peri with him? Okay, no problems! Nip off with Turlough. . . you needn't sing this time. . . and go to **48**.

44

The monkish figure ahead of the three of you stops. He sweeps aside the carpet curtain. He ushers you forward. You step into a gigantic hall with huge mullioned windows. It is lit by hundreds of candles, guttering in the draught.

Peri shivers. 'Freezing, isn't it?'

'*Peri*shing,' you smile back.

Then something wipes the smile off your face. You catch sight of a line of black-shirted Golons standing behind a long table. At the head of the table, gagged and bound, sits the Doctor. Standing proudly, by him, are the three henchmen, The Boss, Fritz and Hans.

The monk raises his arm. He points to the archway. At this sign, the Golons move to cut off your retreat.

Garth turns to you all. He raps out, 'Tell us where the TARDIS is! The Doctor won't talk. Perhaps you will?' His evil eye swivels until it stops at you, Chris.

'Ah, you're Chris, aren't you? Yes, my wife — The Queen, you know — told me your name. Right, Chris, cross-question him!'

Playing for time, Turlough jokes, 'I've heard of cross-questioning, but never criss-cross-questioning!'

The Golons chatter menacingly. They don't see the joke — just blood! You cough and try to look as if you are going to tell Garth Hadeez where the TARDIS is. 'Well, you go down past "Ye Werewolf's Fang". . . '

Out of the corner of your eye you see Peri slip her hand into her pocket. She gives you a clue of what she's up to, by saying to Garth: 'I'll *lay sir*, he knows!' You pick up the clue: she's going for her laser gun.

You play for time. You step up to the Doctor. You say slowly, 'If you'll remove the gag, I'm sure the Doctor will talk.'

The monk points at a Golon, Then at you. You shut your eyes.

Go to **49**.

45

Bad choice, Chris! You start dodging about. You make a great leap to safety to your left. You have overshot. . . and find yourself falling, falling into the bowl of the crater. When you come round you find yourself looking up into the beautiful, scary eyes of. . . Queen Tyrannica. You are her slave for life. That is, you have lost your life.

You couldn't do better than start a new adventure.

THE END

46

Meanwhile you are keeping a sharp look-out over on the radar scan screen. Suddenly something suspicious catches your eagle eye. Could it be Garth's rocket lander sitting there in a crater on Phobos? You call the Doctor over. 'Doctor, have a look-see!'

The Doctor crosses the Control Room, muttering to himself, 'They're in *Gulliver's Travels*, y'know.'

'What are?' you ask.

'The moonlets of Mars,' the Doctor says. 'Phobos and Deimos. Did you know they were named after Mars, god of war's horses, who pulled his chariot — '

He breaks off as he sees the screen with its greenish glow. He bangs the bench worktop with his fist.

'By Hades!' he cries. 'Why didn't you tell me before, Chris? Letting me chunter on. . . like that. . . '

'Oh tush!' Peri flatters him. 'You *never* chunter on, Doctor.'

With dazzling swiftness the Doctor programs the TARDIS to land on Phobos. 'In the *next* crater,' he adds.

'Not in the crater with the critter!' Peri chortles.

'Action stations!' the Doctor orders. And the TARDIS begins its clanking-wailing descent onto Phobos.

'Chris!' he calls out. 'Keep your eyes skinned for any activity near Garth's rocket lander. Tell me if the natives are restless, won't you?'

Turlough checks the equipment. Peri comes over to look at the radar scan screen.

'What's that, Chris?' she says leaning on your shoulder.

'If it's what I think it is,' you say breathlessly, 'it looks remarkably like — '

'GARTH HADEEZ!' you shout together, 'coming out of his rocket lander.'

'Well, Chris,' the Doctor asks, 'are you going to go boldly forth where no man has dared to go before?'

Then go to **8**.

47

False alarm! It isn't the Black Hole. If it were, that would be the end of this adventure. And any others. For it would suck you, the Doctor, Peri, Turlough and the TARDIS into it.
Go to **51** *and consider your options.*

48

'Which way to the castle?' you ask Turlough.

Turlough produces his pocket micro. He punches in the right keys to search its Mega-Memory Store. In less than a nanosecond its mini-screen displays a map of Prague in the early

1600s. He studies it for a moment. Then he snaps it to OFF and points up the hill.

'We nip up the hill. Left at "Ye Werewolf's Fang". Right at the stake. And it's at the top of Kafka Lane.'

You set off at a good cross-country trot. 'Just like the school run!' Turlough puffs. You both follow the directions and, sure enough, at the top of Kafka Lane you see it. The gaunt outline of a huge castle. Its craggy outline is lit up fitfully by the moon as the clouds scud in front of it.

You cross a wooden drawbridge. You come to a huge oak door. You pull the chain. You hear slow dragging footsteps. Through a slit window by the door you spy a chink of candlelight. There is a rattling of heavy chains. A bolt is drawn back. A key turns in the rusty lock. The great door creaks open.

There stands a huge thick-set figure in a monk's cowl and hood which conceals his face. All you glimpse is a single gleaming eye glinting under the hood.

'He's thick. . . as the door!' Turlough whispers to you.

'Thicker!' you hiss back,.

The figure beckons you in. It leads the way to a vast archway, covered with a heavy curtain of carpet. The door slams behind you.

You turn. There Peri stands beside an empty knight in armour. She steps out to join you on tip- toe. The monk, ahead of you, does not notice.

Go to **44.**

49

Something heavy slumps on the floor beside you. You open your eyes. The Golon is slumped at your feet. You quickly take in what's happened. Peri has pulled out her laser gun and shot the Golon. At that, all the other Golons take flight. In the confusion you untie the Doctor.

You leap forward to the monk. You pull back his hood.

'Garth Hadeez himself!' you cry in astonishment.

'Just as I thought,' the Doctor says. 'I'm afraid I wasn't fooled, Garth, one moment by your monk's cowl.'

'Or his one-eyed monk scowl!' Peri chortles.

'Grab him!' the Doctor calls out.

But Garth is too quick for you all. He leaps towards the big window. Turlough grapples with him. In the struggle Turlough pushes Garth through the window. He plummets to the watery moat twenty metres below. There is a great splash. You rush to the broken window. You see Garth striking out for the bank of the moat.

'He's getting out of the moat, Doctor!' you yell.

'After him!' the Doctor shouts.

The four of you hare out through the archway. You heave open the huge oak door. You cross the drawbridge just in time to see Garth's personal mini-rocket take off into the night sky.

'He's got away — drat it!' the Doctor says.

'And I bet I know where he's headed for. The head of Halley's Comet! I suppose you know what that means? He won't be back in this part of the Milky Way for at least another seventy-five years!'

Tired and weary you all wend your way back to the TARDIS. As you go the Doctor tells you: 'Chucking people out of windows was a popular sport in Prague in those, er, these days. Defenestration, they called it. It was such an incident that began the Thirty Years' War. You'll find it in the history books.'

'Will you find the defenestration of Garth in the books, Doctor?' you ask.

'Er, no!' the Doctor says. 'Nor about our visit to Mr Kepler. It's all been CENSORED, you see.'

'Nothing about Garth?' you cry in amazement.

'Well,' the Doctor says, as you clamber into the welcome warmth of the TARDIS. 'There is one story about him. He's an extraterrestrial, you see. In the twentieth century they made a film about him. Called, I believe, *ET*. But it was nothing like Garth Hadeez.'

THE END.

50

The four of you make a wide detour round the
Queen and her Golon stragglers.

'Let's cut off their retreat!' the Doctor says.

You alone, Chris, push on ahead of the Doctor
and his two friends. Suddenly from behind an ice
dune something hideous rears it ugly mug — Garth
Hadeez! His single red eye fixes on you. You feel
like a rabbit caught in a car's headlights. Next a
horrible hissing sounds behind you. You glance
round to see it is Queen Tyrannica herself.

Is all lost? What will you do?
Make a dash for it? Go to **58.**
Use your Swiss Army knife? Go to **59.**

51

One Martian leap — of thirty metres or so; nothing
to boast about on Mars — brings you to the very
door of the TARDIS. You hurl yourself through
the door. You land at the Doctor's feet. Turlough
slams the door. Peri helps you up and gives you a
reviving cup of Tang. The Doctor puts the
TARDIS into lift-off.

Amid the usual clanking and wailing of take-off
you ask the Doctor, 'What made the Golon stop?
Just as he was about to clobber me?'

'Oh,' The Doctor says airily, 'I merely jammed
Garth Hadeez's orders with sonic beams. Then I
countermanded Hadeez's orders with the Babel

Master. Told the Golon to lie doggo. Simple.
When you know how.'

Peri has aimed the radar scan camera at the
rocket base in the crater. Suddenly she shouts,
'Doctor! I think he's taking off!'

'Taking off what?' the Doctor asks. 'His pants!'

'No, Doctor,' Peri says in exasperation.
'Y'know, 5–4–3–2–1. Blast-off!'

On the scan they see clouds of steam and flame
billow out from beneath the rocket. Golons march
off, followed by Garth Hadeez and his Queen. The
Maggots are left swarming round the launch pad —
presumably to die. The rocket begins lift-off. It
gathers speed slowly. Then it disappears OFF
CAMERA.

'I wonder where the devil the devil's going to put
that Black Hole?' the Doctor wonders.

'Can't we get a fix on it, Doctor?' Turlough asks.

'No point, Turlough,' the Doctor says. 'A Black
Hole sucks everything into itself. Matter, gravity,
light rays — you name it! No point in firing radar
beams at it. They won't bounce back off it. Just get
sucked into the cosmic plug hole. . . '

'Eek!' Peri exclaims. 'What happens if one of us
got sucked in?'

'You get spaghettified!' the Doctor says. 'Pulled
out into a long, hollow tube. Macaronified, if you
prefer. A Black Hole's like a cosmic Cheshire Cat.
Even as you look at it, the light rays that let you
look at it disappear into the cat itself. So the cat

52

vanishes leaving only a grin behind. A gravity grin.'

'Like the cat that lapped gravy for tea!' Peri quips.

'Why?' you ask.

'Because,' Peri chuckles, 'he has a gravy-tea grin!'

'Sorry to butt in,' Turlough calls out, 'but there's a UFO on the screen.'

The Doctor takes one look at a round green object on the radar scan screen.

'Mmmm,' he says thoughtfully. 'It could be the moonlet Phobos. Or it could be that Black Hole in orbit already.'

Which do you think it is?
Phobos? Go to **7**.
The Black Hole? Go to **47**.

52

You square up to the mighty Golon. You go for your stungun. But you are not quick enough. Several more Golons surround you. They overpower you. They carry you off down into the bowl of the crater. They present you to the Queen. She flutters her wings and her eyelids at you. Then she speaks your doom.

'Oh, Chris! You shall be my hairdresser.'

You look aghast at her writhing nest of snakes growing out of her head.

Perhaps you'd better begin a new adventure.
Go back to 2.

53

It's a comet, Doctor!' you shout. 'Look at its fiery tail.'

'Not fiery,' the Doctor says. 'Quite the opposite. Freezy. Icy. And dusty. And do you see? It's tail points away from the Sun. Know why?'

'Sir, *sir*!' Turlough hisses, shooting his hand up as if he were answering not a Time Lord but a Time-Table Lord, a schoolmaster. (A far more terrifying person!) 'Because the dust in its tail gets hot from the Sun and sort of rises like smoke in a chimney, sir.'

'Never!' Peri coos. 'It's because the darling little specks of dust ride away from the Sun on a lovely shining sunbeam.'

'Well, Chris?' the Doctor fixes you with a steely stare. 'Who's right? Turlough or Peri?'

If you think Turlough's right, go to 37.
If you think Peri is, go to 34.

54

Wowee! This is fun! The Rover zooms over the chasm. Just like in a James Bond movie. You look down at Phobos below you. You've cleared the crater now. Should be making touchdown any second.

Hey! What's happening? You see Phobos dwindling. Help! You are in orbit. Round and round Phobos, once round every hour or so.

That's the end of this little adventure, Chris.
Go back to 2 and consider your options.

55

'No,' she said. 'Left.'

Go back to 14 and consider your options.

56

The shadow falling on yours raises its fist. You can see its fist has a hook-like claw. It is poised above the shadow of your head. You shut your eyes. You put on an extra spurt. You open them again. . .

And the shadow has gone! You stop. You turn round. There, sprawled in the pink dust, is the Golon, your would-be attacker. But there's no time to look closer. Fast behind him are coming a line of Golons. They are out for your blood.

You turn away from the horrible sight. You sprint at top speed for the TARDIS. You hear the Golons snorting and stamping like enraged bulls behind you. Turlough's voice comes to you across the dunes. 'Don't give up, Chris! Only another thirty metres!'

The Golons are gaining on you! You can hear their gargling growing nearer.

What are you going to do?
Make one great Martian leap for safety? (You might overshoot!) Go to **51**.
Dodge about in the dunes? Go to **45**.

57

The four of you plough over the ice towards the city Garth has built on Halley's Comet. Soon there towers before you the silvery rocket you first spied when you landed.

The Doctor takes out his transponder device. He sets it up and aims it at the rocket's cone. He fires a beam of deadly theta rays at it.

'That'll put paid to Garth's plans to dominate the galaxy!'

'But how, Doctor?' you ask.

'I've blown the inertial guidance system — for good!' the Doctor laughs. 'But Garth won't discover it till he's taken off. When — heh! heh! — it'll be too late!'

The four of you merrily make your way back to the TARDIS. Once inside, the Doctor says with a chuckle: 'I fancy that's the last we'll see of Garth Hadeez and his hateful Queen Tyrannica!'

'And the Golons!' Peri says.

'What's left of 'em,' Turlough laughs.

The Doctor turns to you. 'Well done, Chris! Don't know what we'd've done without your invaluable help. The Galaxy — the Milky Way, I mean — can hurtle through the universe in peace again.' He shakes your hand. Then adds: 'Any time you feel like another adventure, you know what to do, don't you?'

He means, go back to 2.

58

You run like billio. But you are no match for Garth and his Queen. They easily catch up with you. They close in. . . and that is that, Chris: the end of this adventure for you.

Go back to 2 and begin a new adventure.

59

You draw your Swiss Army knife. The Queen laughs cruelly. 'Huh! You don't honestly think a pocket knife can scare me, do you?' she sneers.

Garth glances at his Queen. A smug smile plays on his plug-ugly mug until a steely look from her wipes it off again.

'Little do they know!' you think. With a deft flick you open your knife. Garth makes to stop you. But the Queen freezes him with another look. 'Let our enemy have some fun!' she jeers.

'Thank you,' you say, bowing low. At the same time you unfold the knife just like a robot toy into an exact replica of Garth Hadeez himself.

'Oh, *no*!' the Queen shrieks in horror. 'Not *another* Garth! I couldn't stand it!' She backs off in

terror. Garth dutifully follows her, lumbering off as fast as he can to catch her up.

You get your breath back. Then you feel a friendly pat on your back. It is the Doctor, with his two young friends.

'Well done, Chris!' the Doctor beams at you. 'You certainly put the wind up them. But quick! After them!'

'What, *now*?' Turlough cries, echoing your very thoughts.

'Yes, Turlough, now. Before they take off in their rocket!'

Go to 57.

60

The Queen looks furious. Her scary phizog seems to say, 'How dare you win!' She snaps her long talons. A team of Golons step out of the ice cave. She sweeps her arms together, displaying her blue butterfly wings. The knives on it glint menacingly at you. She makes a large 'O' with her arms. The Golons dutifully obey her. They surround you.

'It's all up now!' you think. But you haven't reckoned on the Doctor. With Peri and Turlough he comes racing to the rescue. He picks the Golons off with small stungun fire. The Queen orders those Golons still standing to retreat.

Do you follow them? Go to 50.

Or do you go to Garth's city? Go to 57.

61

You find the Rover. You get into the driving seat, switch on and the engine roars into life. You set off. Then the engine dies on you.

Go to 18.

62

You've gone left when you should have gone straight on past the gibbet. You go back to the gibbet.
Now, which way do you turn at the gibbet?
Left? Go to 69.
Right? Go to 64.

63

Wrong, Chris. Go to the stake! No, seriously, go back to the stake. Go to 30 and consider your options.

64

Correct. Go to 30.

65

You've gone right when you should have gone straight on past the gibbet. You go back to the gibbet.
Now, which way do you turn at the gibbet?
Left? Go to 66.
Right? Go to 67.

66

You leave the crater. You skirt round it to a dune. You hide behind it. From its safety you watch what the Golons are going to do with Garth. Ah! They are making for a shiny red Rover, a sort of Martian Beach Buggy for buzzing about Phobos in.

Can you get to the Rover before the Golons?
If you think you can, go to 18.
If not, go to 19.

67

No, wrong again, Chris. That would take you back along the route you've just come.
Go back to 26 and consider your options.

68

Unwise decision, Chris. You bound forward to grab the flaming torch from the Boss. Try as you may to wrest the flaming thing from his grasp, you can't. He is too strong for you. In a flash his assistants have you roped and tied next to Peri on the huge funeral pyre of brushwood and logs. Take a tip from the Doctor. He says: 'Leave it to me.'
Go to 43.

69

No, wrong again. That would take you back along the route you've just come.
Go back to 26 and consider your options.

70

The Doctor homes in on the object on the radar screen.

'Definitely!' he says. 'It's Garth Hadeez's mother ship! I'm going to send out laser waves. They'll block the direction-finding apparatus on Garth's space-ship. Then I shall guide the ship towards that Black Hole we located earlier.'

So saying, he programs the TARDIS to carry out his instructions to the number. Finally he switches on the TARDIS's Scrambler Machine. Full power! This completely disorients Garth's mother-ship. The last you see of her is heading straight for the Black Hole.

'Good riddance to bad rubbish!' Turlough shouts gleefully.

'And so say all of us!' Peri and you chorus.

'And that is the end of this little adventure,' the Doctor says. He shakes you by the hand. 'Thanks for coming along, Chris!'

THE END